Newspapers

C000197009

Finish this newspaper's front page.

This newspaper has some things missing. Read the story and add these 3 things:

① An exciting headline — to make it look important.

③ An exciting picture.

② An introduction to explain where the frog came from.

Daily Blah

①
....
....

②
....
....

③

The giant frog has been causing lots of damage in the South-East of England.

The frog is 3 m long and weighs 1 tonne.

It has been crushing cars, and eating pets.

The police are using helicopters to try to capture the frog. They are trying to catch it using a giant net.

PRACTISE MAKING WORDS STAND OUT

In your word-processor program, make a list of 10 things that you find really scary. Then change the size of the text so that the scarier the thing, the bigger it is. Put the scariest thing into **bold** and CAPITALS.

Put Things in Order

A story would be very confusing if the end came before the beginning.

That's why it's important for a story to be in the right order.

Things in the Wrong Order are Confusing

Jokes have to be in the right order too. This joke's been muddled up.

It doesn't make any sense.

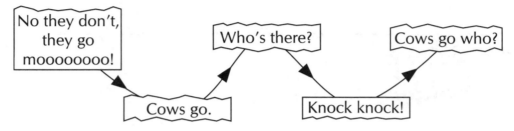

No they don't, they go mooooooo!	Who's there?	Cows go who?
Cows go.	Knock knock!	

It's Better to Put Things in the Right Order

The joke is easier to understand if it's in the right order.

(But it still isn't very funny.)

Knock knock!
Who's there?
Cows go.
Cows go who?
No they don't, they go mooooooo!

The Right Order is Important for Lots of Things

Jokes are better if you tell them in the right order.

These things are also better if they're in the right order:

1 A set of instructions.

2 A history book.

3 A telephone book.

REMEMBER

When you write a story for your newspaper,

don't start at the end and finish at the beginning.

Put Things in Order

① Why is it bad when stories are in the wrong order?

....

② Which of these need to be in the right order?

Tick the ones that are better if they're in the right order.

☑ A story

☐ A dictionary

☐ An address book

☐ A recipe

☐ A diary

③ Put this poem in the right order.

Rewrite this short poem in the right order.

> And wave it about,
> Said the waiter, "Don't shout!
> There was an old person from Crewe,
> Or the rest will be wanting one too!"
> Who found a dead mouse in his stew.

....

....

....

....

Cut and Paste

Word processors make it easy for you to move words around.

This means it's easy to put things in the right order.

Use 'Cut' and 'Paste' to Move Things Around

This joke is all mixed up.

> Just pull yourself together.
> Doctor doctor!
> I feel like a pair of curtains.

But it's easy to rearrange on a computer.

Just use 'Cut' and 'Paste' from the 'Edit' menu...

...or use the 'Cut' and 'Paste' buttons.

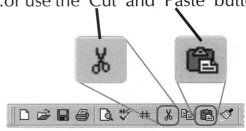

(Your 'Cut' and 'Paste' buttons might look different.)

'Cut' and 'Paste' are Easy to Use

 Highlight the words you want to move.

Then click on 'Cut'.

 The words disappear.

> Just pull yourself together.
> Doctor, doctor!
> I feel like a pair of curtains.

 Click the cursor where you want to put the words.

> Doctor, doctor!
> I feel like a pair of curtains.

 Click on 'Paste'.

The words reappear.

> Doctor, doctor!
> I feel like a pair of curtains.
> Just pull yourself together.

Cut and Paste

① What are 'Cut' and 'Paste' used for?

....

....

② Which menu contains 'Cut' and 'Paste'?

Draw a circle around the correct answer.

File   View   Help

Edit   Tools

③ How do you use 'Cut' and 'Paste'?

What is the correct order for these sentences?

A   Click on 'Paste'.

B   Highlight the text you want to move.

C   Click on 'Cut'.

D   Click where you want to move the text to.

First: ....

Second: ....

Third: ....

Fourth: ....

COMPUTER TASK... (This one is good to do in pairs.)

Get a partner to type in **five important historical events**.
Things like: World War Two, the Battle of Hastings, FIVE splitting up, Jesus being born...
Now you have to **cut and paste** them into the right order (the order that they happened in).
When you've done it, swap roles and do it again.

Changing Words

Interesting words can make a story much nicer to read.

Interesting Words Make a Story Less Boring

These passages tell the same story. The one on the left is a bit boring.
But the one on the right has a few extra words that make it much better.

> The wizard picked up his magic wand. He waved it through the air and spoke the words of the magic spell.
> There was a puff of smoke. The mouse shook, then was turned into a swan.

> The **young** wizard picked up his **mysterious** magic wand. He waved it **quickly** through the air and **quietly** spoke the words of the **strange** magic spell.
> There was a **sudden** puff of **pink** smoke.
> The **frightened** mouse shook, then was turned into a **beautiful white** swan.

Use Words that Make Things Easy to Imagine

 'Mysterious' and 'strange' make you think of magic.

 'Frightened' helps you imagine how something is feeling.

 'Young', 'beautiful' and 'white' make it easy to imagine how things look.

 'Quickly' and 'sudden' can make you feel excited
— like when things are happening very fast.

You can Add, Change or Delete words

1. **Add** words by clicking the cursor somewhere and typing.

2. **Change** a whole word by **double-clicking** on it to **highlight** it.
   When you type the new word, the original word will disappear.

3. **Deleting** words means removing them. You can either:
   a. **Delete a whole word** by highlighting it then pressing 'Backspace',
   b. **Delete one letter at a time** by clicking the cursor somewhere and pressing 'Backspace'.

   This is the 'Backspace' key — it might have an arrow on it.

Changing Words

① Why is it good to use interesting words in a story?

....

③ What do these sentences become?

What will these sentences become when I press the keys below?

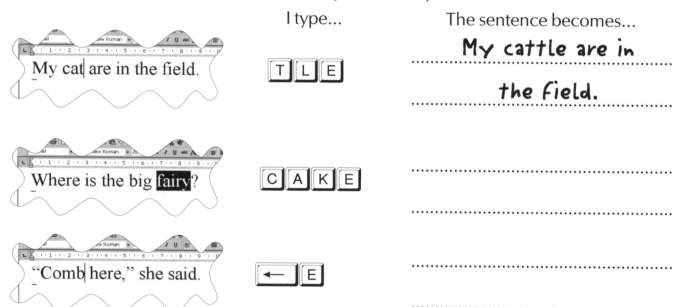

	I type...	The sentence becomes...
My cat are in the field.	T L E	My cattle are in the field.
Where is the big fairy?	C A K E	....
"Comb here," she said.	← E	....

PRACTISE CHANGING WORDS

Look at the passage below. Type it into your word processor.

Now **edit the passage** to make it more exciting.

Double-click on boring words and type better words.

Click in the text and **add** extra words of your own.

You could even change whole sentences if you want.

My friend Dom is a jungle explorer. He smells because he wears the same clothes every day. The jungle is a scary place. It has creatures like tarantulas and snakes. Every day is an adventure. In a single day he might fight a snake, get trapped in a big spider's web, be chased by monkeys and fall in a swamp. Once, he met a tribe living in the jungle. He thought they were nice until they put him in a pot and started to cook him.

Spellcheckers

Computers can help you spell everything correctly.

Spellcheckers Help You Find Mistakes...

Sometimes the mistakes are
underlined automatically.

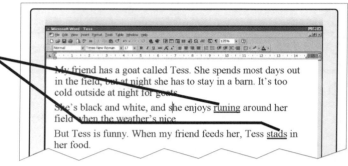

Sometimes you have to click
on the spellcheck button.

It might look like this one.

...But You Still Need to Know How to Spell

Spellcheckers usually ask you to
choose the correct spelling from a list.

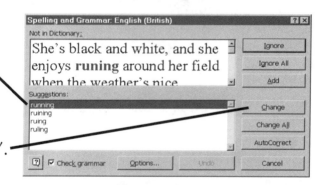

Click the correct spelling
and then click on 'Change'.

This means you still need to know how to spell.

Spellcheckers Can't Always Help

Spellcheckers are good... but they can't find every mistake.

The name of my friend's coat is Tess.

A spellchecker won't know that you mean 'goat' — not 'coat'.

'Coat' is a real word, so the spellchecker thinks it's okay.
You need to make sure the text makes sense.

You still need to know how to find spellings — even if you have a spellchecker.

Spellcheckers

① Spellcheck this document.

The spellchecker finds 3 spelling mistakes in this document. Draw an arrow pointing at each correct spelling. The first one has been done for you.

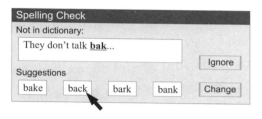

My best friends are trees. When I feel unhappy, I talk to the trees. They don't talk bak... they just lissen. And sumtimes, after I've told them why I feel so unhappy, I don't feel unhappy any more. That's why trees are my friends.

② Will a spellchecker help?

These sentences all have mistakes in them. Circle the word that's wrong.
Then tick the box if a spellchecker will find the mistake. Use a dictionary if you need.

Will a spellchecker find the mistake?

(a) This book is great — I can't put it (downe.)
I read it whenever I have any spare time.

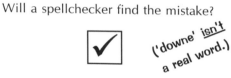 ('downe' isn't a real word.)

(b) This (took) is great — I can't put it down.
I read it whenever I have any spare time.

(c) This book is great — I can't put it down.
I read it whenever I have any xpare time.

PRACTISE SPELLCHECKING...

Here's a good way to practise: Ask your teacher for a word-processor file that has some mistakes in. Now you have to **use the spellchecker** to find all the mistakes you can. Spellcheckers can't pick up **all mistakes**. When you've finished spellchecking, have a read through and see if you can spot any more mistakes that the spellchecker missed.

Find and Replace

You can use 'Find' and 'Replace' to make lots of changes to a document.

Sometimes I Make Lots of Mistakes...

This is part of a very long story about Ally.

But Ally isn't a boy, she's a girl.
And Ally isn't a dog, she's a cat.

Woof

> Ally is the name of my dog. He's a very good dog. He's black, and he likes sitting on my lap. When I'm in the kitchen, he asks me to give him food. And when I stroke him, he purrs — that's how I know he's happy.

...and I Need to Make Lots of Changes

I need to change 'he' to 'she' everywhere in the story.
And I need to make some other changes too.

If I made all the changes myself, it would
take a long time, and I'd probably miss some.

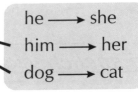

he ⟶ she
him ⟶ her
dog ⟶ cat

Use 'Replace' to Swap One Word for Another

A computer can change 'he' to 'she' everywhere in the story very quickly.
But you need to be very careful — the computer can get 'confused'.

Change 'he' to 'she' — this works fine.

he likes sitting on my lap ⟶ **she** likes sitting on my lap

But the computer gets
confused and wants to change 'the'...

Ally is t**he** name of my dog ...to 'tshe'... Ally is t**she** name of my dog

...because 'the' contains the word 'he'.

Some word processors will let you replace 'whole words only'. This means that the computer only looks for 'he' on its own, and not as part of another word.

Advantages of using 'Replace'
1. It's much quicker.
2. It doesn't miss any words.

Disadvantages of using 'Replace'
It can change words you don't want to change.

Unit 4A — Writing for Different Audiences

Find and Replace

① What's good and bad about using 'Replace'?

'Replace' is useful if you need to swap one word for another.
Give two advantages of using 'Replace'.

1. ....

2. ....

But 'Replace' also has a disadvantage. What is this?

....

....

② Which word will confuse the computer?

I use 'Replace' to change some words.
Circle the words in these sentences which will confuse the computer.

I change 'oats' to 'barley'. → We all put on our ⟨coats,⟩ and headed towards the farm.

I change 'art' to 'science'. → Apart from art, I like most subjects at school.

I change 'hot' to 'cold'. → The film was shot in the Sahara Desert, and so the temperature was very hot.

Change 'is' to 'was'. → The first part of this test is about multiplication and division.

Using Find and Replace

'Find and Replace' is great. This is how you use it.

Be careful with 'Replace All' — Computers get Confused

① Go to the 'Edit' menu, and click on 'Replace'.

In some programs, it's called 'Change'.

② I want to change 'he' to 'she'.

So I type 'he' here...

...and 'she' here.

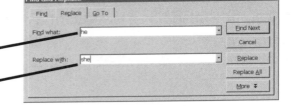

③ It's usually best to use 'Find Next' (and **not** 'Replace All'). Then you can check that the computer's not getting confused and changing the wrong thing.

- I don't want to change this one — so I click on 'Find Next'.

'he' is part of the word 'the'.

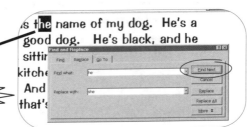

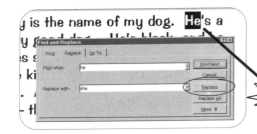

- But I do want to change this one — so I click on 'Replace'.

Change 'he' to 'she'.

Sometimes it's Okay to Use 'Replace All'

You can use 'Replace All' to change some words.

My pet duck is called Quacker. Quacker is white with orange legs.

I like Quacker because she makes me laugh.

Actually, my duck's name is Boris.
I need to replace 'Quacker' with 'Boris'.

Quacker won't be part of another word.
This means the computer can't get confused.
You **can** use 'Replace All' here.

Using Find and Replace

① Finish these sentences using words from the grey box.

| Replace All | Change | Edit |

1. You can find 'Replace' on the .... menu.

2. Another word for 'Replace' is ....

3. You have to be careful when you use the button marked ....

② Should you use 'Replace All' to change these words?

Draw a happy face next to the sentence where I could use 'Replace All'.
For the others, draw vampire fangs on any words that will confuse the computer.

Change 'read' to 'write'.

I read a book every week. When I finish each book, I'm ready to start a new one.

Change 'car' to 'van'.

They carried all the heavy equipment to the car, and then went to the golf course.

Change 'lip' to 'cheek'.

I slipped on the banana skin and cut my lip.

Change 'Madonna' to 'Britney'.

Madonna was touring the UK, so I bought a ticket for her concert.

PRACTISE FIND AND REPLACE

Write a funny story about someone called **Ben.**
Now change the story so that it's about a girl instead — use **find and replace** to change Ben to a girl's name. **Read** the story, does it make sense now?
You'll need to replace other words too, like **he** with **she**, **his** with **her** and so on...

 **Computer Activity**   ## Write a Recipe

You'll need a word processor for this project.

In this project you will:

Write a recipe for a class cookbook.

> Use ideas from this unit to make your recipe look fantastic.
> ✓ Your recipe needs to be interesting, and make people want to cook it.
> ✓ It also has to look good.

Writing the recipe

a) You need to think of what you're going to cook.
It doesn't have to be a proper recipe. It could be something you've made up, like 'Dragon and Walrus Tasty Bake'.

b) You need a list of ingredients. Again, you can make some of these up — maybe you like eating old carrier bags, for example.

c) Then you need to write down all the things you have to do.
Make these into a list of instructions.

d) Your recipe has to be easy to follow, so make all your instructions really clear.

Type it into a word processor

 You need to type your recipe into a word processor.

 You don't have to type it all in at once.

 You can do a bit, save your work and then come back to it another time.

Save your recipe

You need to save your recipe if you want to work on it again.
Write the name of the file here.

Write a Recipe

Finish the text first...

It's best to get the text right first — don't worry about how it looks until you're happy with what you've written.

Get the words right...

• Make your recipe really clear.

• Use 'Replace' if you need to — maybe you got one of the ingredients wrong.

• And make sure you use the spellchecker.

...and put all the steps in the right order

• Decide what the main steps in the recipe are.

• You can change the order of these using 'Cut' and 'Paste'.

...and then Make it Look Cool

When you've finished writing your recipe, you can make it look dead cool.
Try to make it look like the recipes you see in magazines.

• Think of a really interesting name for your recipe — and make it really **BIG** so that it stands out.

• Do an exciting picture to go with your recipe. You could do this on a computer (see Unit 4B) or you could draw one on a piece of paper.

• Make these headings bigger than the text that comes after them.

• But don't forget, it has to look fantastic.

Scrummy Dog Food Tart

Ingredients
2 tins of dog food
3 eggs
2 packets of crisps
butter

Instructions
1. Open can of dog food.
2. Put into a buttered dish.
3. Separate the egg whites from the yolks.
4. Whisk the egg whites until they go firm.
5. Put on top of the dog food.
6. Cook for 20 minutes, and then top with crisps.

When you've finished your recipe...

 Print it out.

 You could make a class cookbook by putting everyone's recipes together.

 You could even try making a few of the things from the recipes. (If they sound more edible than mine.)

Unit 4A — Writing for Different Audiences

Groovy Things to Do with Pictures

You can make pictures more interesting by repeating bits.

You can Copy Parts of a Picture

You can use Copy and Paste to repeat parts of a picture.
You'll always find them in the Edit menu at the top
(and there may be special Copy and Paste buttons as well).

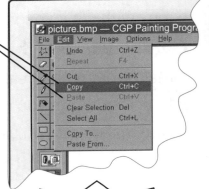

Here are some things you can do:

1) Turn one alien into a crowd of aliens.

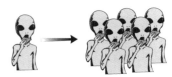

2) Draw a petal then copy it to make a whole flower.

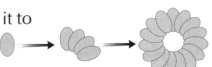

> Try This:
> Select an object, then right-click on it. You might get a menu with Copy and Paste in it.

Copy and Paste are Great for Making Patterns

Patterns are usually made by repeating things.
This is just a simple picture of a bird:

But you can turn it into this:

You can use patterns for:

1) wallpaper,

2) wrapping paper for presents,

3) backgrounds and borders — to make your schoolwork look great.

> Some programs have a **Stamper tool**.
> This makes it much easier to make patterns —
> you just click where you want the pattern to appear.

Groovy Things to Do with Pictures

① Which two words from the Edit menu can help you repeat parts of a picture?

1. .... 2. ....

② How are patterns usually made?

....

③ Write down 3 things that you can use a pattern for:

1. ....

2. ....

3. ....

④ Draw an animal in this square:

⑤ Repeat your picture in each square in this grid:

Make your projects look ace.
Try giving a story a patterned background. Or put a border round a poem.

Selecting Areas to Copy

Remember — you can copy part of a picture. But you have to select it first.

The Select Tool looks like

1) Choose the Select tool.

2) Click and hold the mouse button down to drag a box round part of the picture.

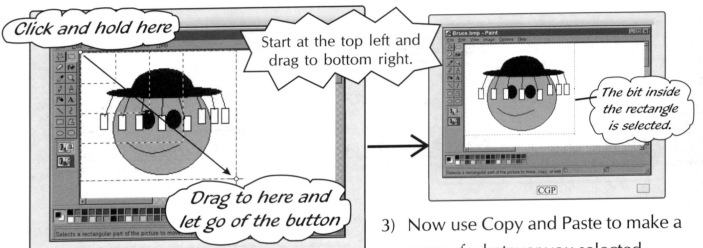

Click and hold here

Start at the top left and drag to bottom right.

The bit inside the rectangle is selected.

Drag to here and let go of the button

3) Now use Copy and Paste to make a copy of whatever you selected.

If you're using *Microsoft Paint*, make sure the "Draw Opaque" tool is turned **OFF**. This means you can select part of the picture without picking up the background.

This is "Draw Opaque".

This is "Don't Draw Opaque".

Just click on the button to choose which you want.

Once you've got that sussed...

This is the "Free-form select tool". It's good for selecting part of a picture.

Ooops! Hit the wrong button? — Press UNDO...

If you make a mistake, here's what to do:

1) Look at the top of the screen for the Undo button.

2) If there isn't one, look in the Edit menu for "Undo".

3) Click on it to **cancel whatever you did last** — magic.

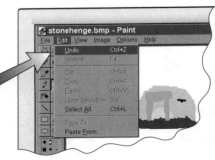

Undo will work in almost any program — it's just the best trick ever.

Questions on Selecting

① What does the Select Tool look like in Microsoft Paint?

There are 2 answers — draw both of them here:

Select Tool	Free-form Select Tool

② Finish this passage about selecting a picture.

Use the words from the cloud to fill in the gaps.

drag
copy
click
select

First you choose the .... tool.

Then you .... and .... a box around

the picture. Then you can .... the picture.

③ Write down two places where you could find Undo.

1. ....

2. ....

④ Help! What should I do?

I've just drawn the Mona Lisa using Microsoft Paint.
Then I deleted it by mistake. Should I...

☐ scream?   ☐ click on Undo?

☐ smile smugly?   ☐ design an aeroplane instead?

(Tick the best answer.)

Selecting things and undoing mistakes — handy tricks indeed...
Yup, these are 2 of the most useful things you can learn. So learn 'em.

 **Computer Activity** # *Build a Fishtank*

You will need a painting or graphics program for this exercise.

In this project you will:

Draw a picture of a fishtank full of fish.

Draw the fishtank

Draw a big rectangle.

Cover most of the screen so you've got plenty of room for fish.

Put some fish in it

Use the Fill tool to colour in the fish.

REMEMBER: Use Undo if the fill leaks. Use the Pencil tool to join up the edges of the fish, then try again.

1) Draw a fish. Make it any colour you like.

2) Select the fish.

3) Copy and Paste it and move it near the first fish.

4) Repeat until you have 6 fish swimming together.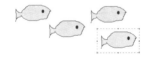

Stick some weed at the bottom

1) Draw a clump of leaves. Colour it green.

2) Make a few copies and put them along the bottom of the tank.

3) Use the Fill tool to colour the big rectangle blue. Ta daa. A full fishtank.

Save your work then print it out

1) Write the name of the file here:

2) Print out your picture and stick it on the wall.

More Fishy Business

Extra Bits for you to Try:

Make some fish in different sizes

1) Open a new document in Paint.

2) Draw a rectangle with a fish in it.

3) Select the fish, then Copy and Paste it and move it into the tank.

4) Click and drag the little square boxes to change the size.

5) Repeat until you have a few different-sized fish.

6) Draw some weed. Colour it green, select it and make different-sized copies along the bottom of the tank.

7) Save the file and write the name here:

8) ... then print it out.

Make some wrapping paper with a fish pattern on it

1) Open a new document.

2) Draw a fish... again. *You'll probably want to choose a nicer colour. I've only got grey.* ☹

3) Copy it, then Paste the copy next to it.

4) Keep going till you have a line of fish along the page.

5) Select the whole line of fish.

6) Copy and Paste the line of fish until you have filled the page.

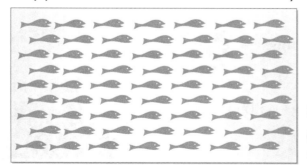

Save it and print it

1) Write the filename here:

2) Print out your wrapping paper and use it to wrap a present.

Making Pictures out of Dots

Here's a great way to make pictures:

Use the Brush Tool to Make a Picture out of Dots

1) You can use the Brush tool to draw dots.

2) Some famous artists (such as Seurat) did oil paintings using dots.

3) You can make interesting effects with dots that you can't do with other pictures.

You Can Change the Thickness of the Brush

1) You can use smaller dots to draw fine details.

2) You can use bigger dots to cover bigger areas.

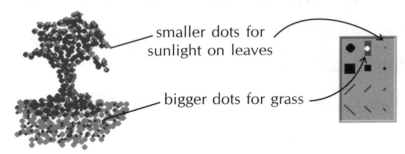

smaller dots for sunlight on leaves

bigger dots for grass

You Can Change the Shape of the Brush

You can get loads of different effects by using different-shaped brushes.

1) You can use round dots to draw fluffy things.

2) You can use a square brush to draw things with corners.

3) You can use lines to draw something spiky.

Making Pictures out of Dots

① *Which tool do you use to draw with dots?*

....

② *Draw a cat's face — just using coloured dots.*

Don't be shy — yours can't be as bad as mine...

③ *Why would you change the thickness of the brush?*

1. ....

....

2. ....

....

④ *What shape of brush would you use to draw:*

a tall skyscraper? ....

a box of pins? ....

a fluffy poodle? ....

It's like finger painting, but without the dirty hands...

 **Computer Activity**   ## *Seeing Dots*

In this project you will:

Make a picture out of dots, squares and lines. Then turn it into a birthday card.

Draw a rectangle to put your picture in

1) Pick the Rectangle tool.

2) Draw a frame for your picture.

It might be easier if you zoom in, using the zoom button. Q

Start with the background

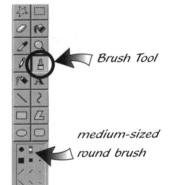

Brush Tool

medium-sized round brush

OK, do some sand first.

1) Pick the Brush tool and choose a medium-sized brush.

2) Click on yellow in the colour chart at the bottom.

3) Draw a load of yellow dots at the bottom of the rectangle. ──────

4) Try using two different shades of yellow — it'll look more interesting.

yeah OK, I know they look like grey dots, but they are yellow, honest...

Use the big brush for the sky, sun and clouds

1) Pick the biggest brush size and click on a pale blue.

2) Fill the rest of the rectangle with big, blue dots.

3) Click on white to make the brush white — then use the brush to make a cloud out of big, white dots.

4) Make the brush yellow then make a sun out of big, yellow dots.

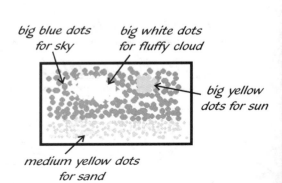

big blue dots for sky   *big white dots for fluffy cloud*

big yellow dots for sun

medium yellow dots for sand

Seeing Dots

Draw a spiky cactus with lines

A cactus usually looks something like this: So you need to make the main bit "blobby" and then add thin spikes to it.

medium-sized line brush

1) Select the big brush tool, and the colour dark green.

2) Draw the shape of the cactus using the big green dots.

3) Change the shape of the brush to a line.

4) Pick a lighter green and draw some spiky lines on the cactus.

5) Try some different lines to get spikes pointing in different directions.

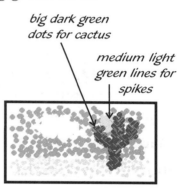

big dark green dots for cactus

medium light green lines for spikes

Use a square brush to make the hut

Buildings are usually easier if you use a square brush — you can get proper corners.

big square brush

1) Pick a square brush — the biggest one is probably best.

2) Choose a brown and draw a building out of squares.

3) Pick a grey colour and draw a roof on top.

slate-grey roof

brown, squarish building

Save it then print it

1) Save the picture. Write the filename here:

2) Print your picture and cut around the rectangle.

3) Take a piece of card and fold it in the middle, then stick your picture on the front.

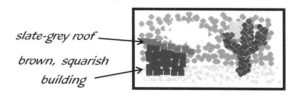

fold here

glue your picture about here — use Pritt Stick or something

write "Happy Birthday" here

4) Don't forget to write your message inside!

Flipping and Rotating

This bit's about making reflections, turning things upside down and spinning things round. In Microsoft Paint, you use the 'Flip/Rotate' tool, which is hidden in the 'Image' menu.

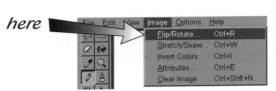

here

"Flip horizontal" reflects it sideways and "Flip vertical" turns it upside down.

1) Click on 'Flip/Rotate' and you'll get a window like this:

2) Click on the thing you want.

3) Hit the OK button.

These two turn it on its side.

This one turns it all the way round (so it's upside down).

You can make Mirror Images using the "Flip" tool

You can make **symmetrical patterns** using reflections of shapes. This pattern is one small picture flipped over and repeated lots of times.

It's easy to make a mirror image of a picture.

1) Draw your picture.

2) Select the picture.

3) Copy and Paste the selection.

4) Use the Flip tool and choose the type of 'flip'.

5) Click OK.

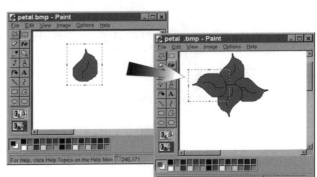

The "Rotate" tool turns things round

"Rotate" means "turn round". You can use the Rotate tool to turn a picture on its side. It's pretty cool — you can make flowers and all sorts. Great.

1) Draw your picture.

2) Select it.

3) Copy and Paste the selection.

4) Use the Rotate tool and choose the type of rotation.

5) Click OK.

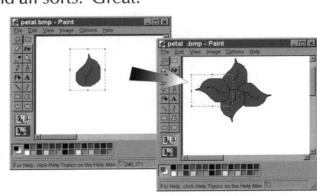

Unit 4B — Making Pictures with Patterns

Flipping and Rotating

① Which menu is the Flip/Rotate tool in? *(in Microsoft Paint)*

It's in the .... menu.

② What does "Flip horizontal" do?

....

....

③ Match each picture with its reflection.

Draw a snake ～～～ from each picture to its correct reflection.

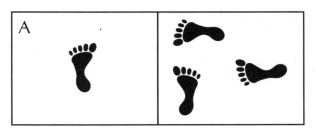

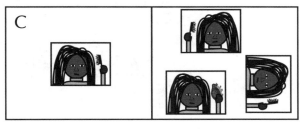

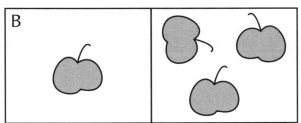

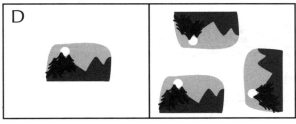

④ Pick the right words in these instructions for rotating a picture. *(in Microsoft Paint)*

Circle the correct answer from each pair.

First you draw a picture and *delete/select* it. Then you *colour/copy* the picture and paste it. Go to the *Image/File* menu and choose *Flip/Rotate Stretch/Skew*. You get another *window/copy* with some choices in it. You can choose what kind of *hairdo/rotation* you want. Then you click *OK/Cancel*.

Save As

Sometimes it's nice to keep loads of different drafts (or versions) of your work. You could:

1) draw a fox and try it with and without a pair of socks,

2) make a pattern and try it in different colours,

3) write a poem and try it with different backgrounds.

> This is a poem
> I wrote it just this morning
> Before I left home
> But I'm afraid

> This is a poem
> I wrote it just this morning
> Before I left home
> But I'm afraid it's really boring.

You can keep old versions using Save As

'Save As' is in the File menu — underneath 'Save'.

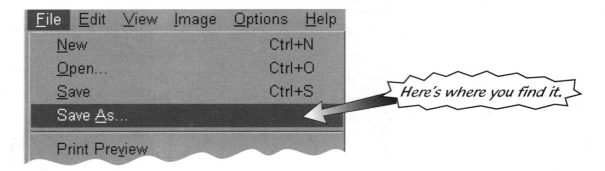

Here's where you find it.

Use Save As to make a new draft of a picture

'Save As' is dead, dead useful. Here's how to use it with pictures:

Picture 1

1) Draw a picture and Save it as "Picture 1".

Picture 2

2) Use 'Save As' to save the picture as "Picture 2".

3) Change one part of the picture, then save your work.

Picture 3

4) Now Save As "Picture 3".

5) Change something else, and save your work again.

If you decide you preferred "Picture 1", you can open it and it'll be just as you left it.

You can make as many versions as you like using 'Save As'.

It's great for trying things out if you're not sure exactly what you want.

Save As

① Name 2 things you can do by keeping different versions of a picture.

1. ....

2. ....

② Which menu is "Save As" in?

....

③ How do you use "Save As"?

Describe how to use Save As to produce 3 versions of a picture.
Write down the 5 steps.

1. ....
   ....

2. ....
   ....

3. ....
   ....

4. ....
   ....

5. ....
   ....

 **Computer Activity** # Stained-Glass Windows

In this project you will:

You'll need tracing paper and colouring pens for the paper bit, and Microsoft Paint for the computer bit.

Design a Stained-Glass Window and try different sets of colours.

Stained-Glass Windows — made of stained (coloured) glass

You'll have seen stained-glass windows before — maybe in a church, or in the front-door panels of someone's house. Here are some examples:

Symmetrical Patterns

Stained-glass windows often use symmetrical patterns.

This window has two main patterns that have been reflected:

  ②

Design your own window — on paper first

Stained-glass designs are easy to make — and they look great.

1. Draw a pattern or picture in this shape.

2. Use tracing paper to copy the shape into shape **A** on the right, then reflect it into shape **B**.

3. Draw a pattern in this square.

4. Use tracing paper to copy it into shape **C**, then reflect it into **D** *(so it's upside down)*.

5. Use a new piece of tracing paper to trace **both** squares **C** and **D** and reflect them into squares **E** and **F**.

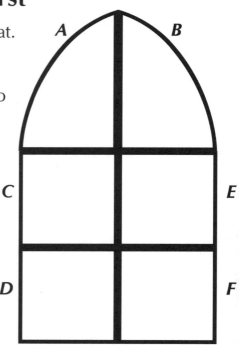

Stained-Glass Windows

Copy your window design onto a computer

1. Open Microsoft Paint and draw a shape like this...

   ... then draw your pattern on it.

   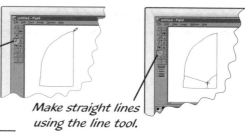

   Use the pencil tool to draw lines.

   Make straight lines using the line tool.

2. Choose the select tool and carefully select the shape...

   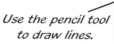

3. Copy and Paste the selection.

   While it's **still** selected, use the Flip/Rotate tool to flip it over.

   It'll **still** be selected, so drag it into place.—

4. Save the design as "BOBwindow1" (but with your name instead of BOB).

5. Now draw a square about this size...

   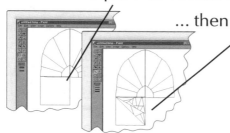

   ... then draw your pattern in it.

6. Select the square and do a Copy and Paste.

   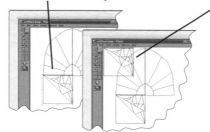

7. Flip the copy over **vertically**, then drag into place.

   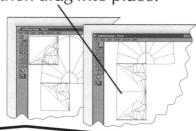

8. Last — select both squares...

   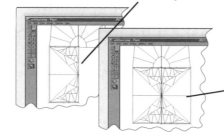

   ... Copy and Paste...

   ... Flip over **horizontally**...

   ... and drag into place.

9. **SAVE IT!**

Colour it in

1. Choose the fill tool and colour in your pattern — then Save As "BOBwindow2".

2. Change a few of the colours and Save As "BOBwindow3".

3. Open "BOBwindow1" again. Try a new set of colours and Save As "BOBwindow4".

4. Carry on making new versions until you find one that you're happy with.

Write the name of your favourite version here:

Tree Diagrams

Tree Diagrams — Questions with Branches

You can use a tree diagram in science to identify plants and animals.

A **tree diagram** can also be called a **key**, a **branched key** or a **branching database**.

EXAMPLE:

Here are four leaves:

This tree diagram shows which plant each one came from.

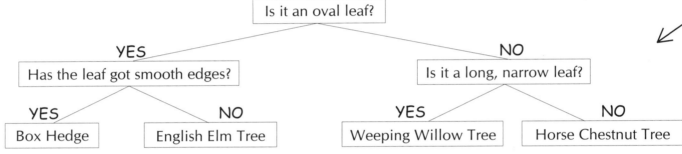

Is it an oval leaf?

YES — Has the leaf got smooth edges?

NO — Is it a long, narrow leaf?

YES — Box Hedge   NO — English Elm Tree

YES — Weeping Willow Tree   NO — Horse Chestnut Tree

You can use Tree Diagrams to Identify Things

A tree diagram can help you identify something that you don't recognise.

1) Arnold is walking through a wood and finds a leaf.
   He wants to know what tree it's from.

 leaf

 Arnold

2) The wood only has elm trees, weeping willows and
   horse chestnut trees, and it's surrounded by a box hedge.

3) He can use the tree diagram above to identify the leaf:

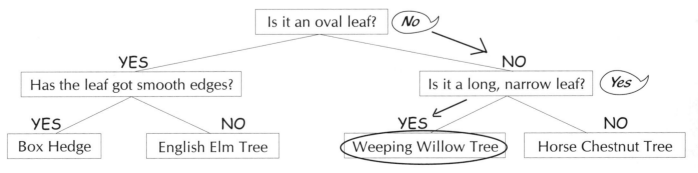

Is it an oval leaf?   *No*

YES — Has the leaf got smooth edges?

NO — Is it a long, narrow leaf?   *Yes*

YES — Box Hedge   NO — English Elm Tree

YES — Weeping Willow Tree   NO — Horse Chestnut Tree

Arnold's leaf is from a **weeping willow** tree.

Tree Diagrams

① Write down another name for a Tree Diagram.

(There are 3 possible answers — you only need to write down one.)

....

② Help Arnold identify these leaves.

Use the key on the left.

   ....

   ....

....

③ Make your own Tree Diagram.

Here are 4 plants and 3 questions.

Azalea Plant

Fir Tree

Oak Tree

Cactus Plant

Does it have spines?

Does it look like a Christmas tree?

Is it a tree?

a)   Work out where the questions should go.
b)   Fill in the answers at the bottom.

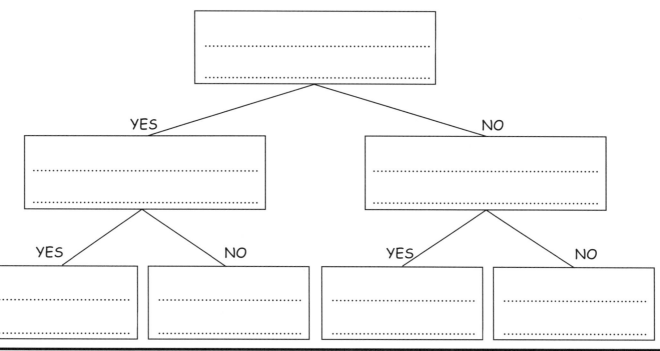

Shapes of Tree Diagrams

Some Tree Diagrams get the Answer Slowly

Here's a tree diagram of 8 animals.

1) To identify the penguin, you need to ask just **2 questions**.

2) But to identify the cat or the ape, you need to ask **5 questions**.

3) It's **not a very good tree diagram** — there are only **8 animals**, but you sometimes have to ask **5 questions** to get to the bottom.

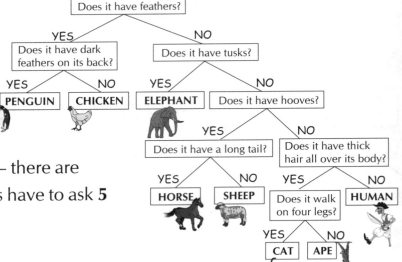

Some Tree Diagrams get the Answer Quickly

1) This is **a better tree diagram** of the same animals.

2) You can identify **any** animal by asking just **3 questions**.

3) Each question splits the remaining animals into 2 **equally-sized** groups.

Does it have four legs?

YES — Does it have a long tail?

NO — Does it have feathers?

YES — Does it have hooves? — YES HORSE / NO CAT

NO — Does it have tusks? — YES ELEPHANT / NO SHEEP

YES — Does it have dark feathers on its back? — YES PENGUIN / NO CHICKEN

NO — Does it have thick hair all over its body? — YES APE / NO HUMAN

4) Tree diagrams work much better that way.

Good Questions Split the Group in Half

1. **Ask questions that will split the group down the middle.**

2. **You'll definitely get rid of half the group that way.**

3. **That's true for each question you ask.**

Shapes of Tree Diagrams

① How many questions do you need to get to the human?

a) Using the first tree on page 36? ....

b) Using the second tree on page 36? ....

② Which of these tree diagrams is better?

Tick the better one.

Is it a bird?
YES ⟋ ⟍ NO

a robin   Is it a plane?
            YES ⟋ ⟍ NO

Concorde   Is it an elephant?
                YES ⟋ ⟍ NO

☐   Jumbo   Superman

Is it a mammal?   ☐
YES ⟋ ⟍ NO

Is it an elephant?   Is it a plane?
YES ⟋ ⟍ NO   YES ⟋ ⟍ NO

Jumbo   Superman   Concorde   a robin

③ How about these?

Tick the better one.

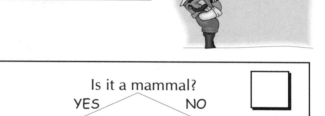

Does the person have blond hair?   ☐
YES ⟋ ⟍ NO

Is the person female?   Does the person have a beard?
YES ⟋ ⟍ NO   YES ⟋ ⟍ NO

Chrissy   Andy   Glenn   Simon

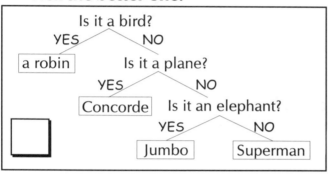

Does the person have a beard?
YES ⟋ ⟍ NO

Glenn   Is the person female?
        YES ⟋ ⟍ NO

☐   Chrissy   Does the person have blond hair?
                      YES ⟋ ⟍ NO

                   Andy   Simon

④ Fill in the missing words in this sentence.

Good questions split the group ....

Identifying Aliens

Use the Tree Diagram to Identify the Aliens

The Aliens:

Follow these Steps for each Alien

1) Start at the top of the tree diagram.

2) Ask yourself the first question.

3) If the answer's "YES", follow the "YES" line. If it's "NO", follow the "NO" line.

4) Ask yourself the next question.

5) If the answer's "YES", follow the "YES" line. If it's "NO", follow the "NO" line.

6) Keep going till you get an answer.

7) Write it down.

The Tree Diagram:

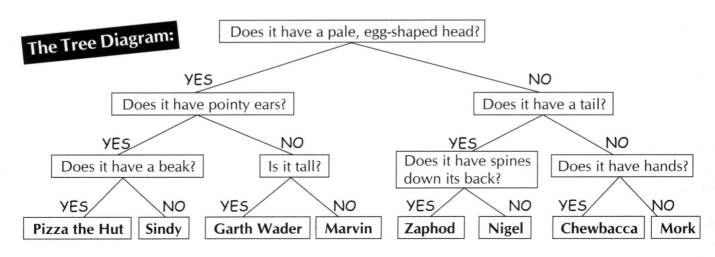

Identifying Aliens

Write the name of each alien in the correct box.

Alien Number 1:

Alien Number 2:

Alien Number 3:

Alien Number 4:

Alien Number 5:

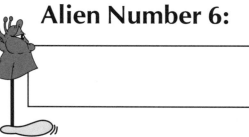

Alien Number 6:

Alien Number 7:

Alien Number 8:

Branching Databases

You can do tree diagrams on a computer — they're called "branching databases".

Here's how to Create a Branching Database

Whatever program you've got, follow these steps:

1. You start by typing in a list of things.

2. Then you type in a question that'll split the group roughly in half.

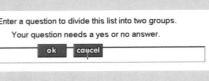

3. Answer that question about everything in your group.

4. The computer uses your answers to put the things into two groups.

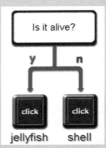

5. For each of the smaller groups you need to think of another question to split it in half.

6. You keep doing this till all the groups are split up and you've just got answers.

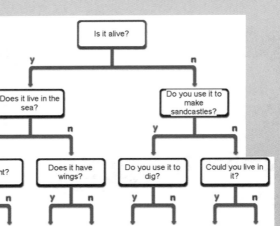

Examples of Branching Database Programs:
Granada Branch, Primary Trees and Branches, BlackCat Decisions, Textease Branch

Branching Databases

① How do you create a branching database?

Fill in the gaps in this list of instructions:

1. Type a ....

2. Type a question that'll .... the group roughly in ....

3. .... that question about everything in your group.

4. The computer uses your answers to put the things into two groups.

5. For each of the smaller groups you need to think of another .... to

....

6. Keep doing this till all the groups are split up and you only have ....

② Which of these are branching database programs?

Draw a squirrel on top of the *right answers.*

Microsoft Word

Granada Branch

BlackCat Logo

Microsoft Excel

Primary Trees and Branches

BlackCat Decisions

Windows Explorer

Granada Spreadsheet

Computer Activity

Make a Musical Tree

In this project you will:

Make a tree diagram for Marvin to identify which musical instrument is which.

Make an information card for each instrument

Choose 8 musical instruments and make information cards for each.

Include a picture and as much information as you can.

EXAMPLE:

Harp:
- has hundreds of strings
- made of wood
- has hundreds of tuning pegs
- is kind of triangle-shaped

You can use the information I've given you (below) or use your own.

INFORMATION:

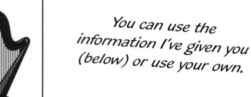

Harp:

made of wood

has hundreds of strings

is kind of triangle-shaped

has hundreds of tuning pegs

Trumpet:

has a mouthpiece

made of brass

has three keys

Violin:

made of wood

has 4 strings

has 4 tuning pegs

has a bow

has a chin rest

reddish-brown colour

Trombone:

has a mouthpiece

made of brass

has no keys

has a slidy thing

Flute:

has a mouthpiece

has loads of keys

has holes

silver colour

Clarinet:

has a mouthpiece

has loads of keys

has holes

black colour

Cello:

made of wood

has 4 strings

has 4 tuning pegs

has a bow

has a floor rest

reddish-brown colour

Triangle:

is triangle-shaped

is made of shiny metal

has no keys, strings or tuning pegs

Make a Musical Tree

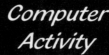

Draw this on a big bit of paper

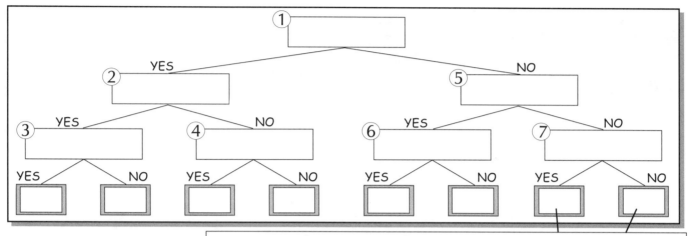

Leave enough space to stick your information cards at the bottom.

Come up with some questions

1. Think of a question that splits the group in half — then write it here.

   Question 1: ....

2. Ask that question about each instrument. Put the cards in separate piles — **yes** or **no**.

3. Look at the "yes" pile. Think of a question that splits that in half (and write it here):

   Question 2: ....

4. Carry on till you've got all 7 questions written:

   Question 3: ....

   Question 4: ....

   Question 5: ....

   Question 6: ....

   Question 7: ....

Stick it all on your Tree Diagram

Write the questions in the numbered question boxes —
then stick the cards in the right places at the bottom of the tree.

 **Computer Activity**

Make a Musical Tree

In this project you will:

Use a Branching Database program to enter your Musical Tree Diagram.

> I'm using Granada Branch. It doesn't matter if you've got a different program — they all work pretty much the same way.

Create a new Branching Database

1. Open Granada Branch.

2. Click on **Make a new Branching Database** and give your database a name.

3. Your screen might look something like this:

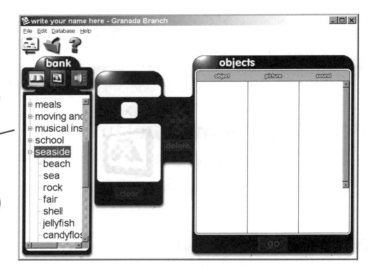

> *Remember — if you're not using Granada Branch, your screen may not look like this.*

4. Type in the list of instruments. In Granada Branch you do it by typing in the box then clicking "add".

5. Click "go" when you've finished the list.

6. You'll get a box to click, then 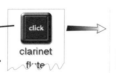 you can type in your first question.

> Enter a question to divide this list into two groups. Your question needs a yes or no answer.
> ok   cancel

7. You'll have to answer the question for all the instruments — so the computer can sort them into two groups.

8. Click to add the next question. Make sure you get the questions in the right place, or it'll go completely pear-shaped.

> *If you mess up and type a question in the wrong place, look for the Edit button. In Granada Branch it looks like this:*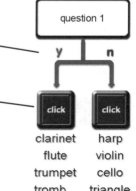

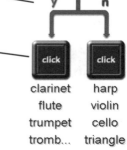

question 1

y   n

click   click

clarinet   harp
flute   violin
trumpet   cello
tromb...   triangle

Make a Musical Tree

Your finished Tree Diagram should look a bit like this:

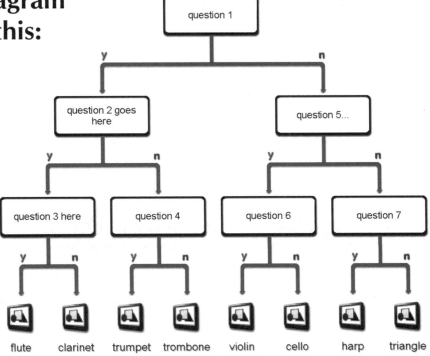

flute   clarinet   trumpet   trombone   violin   cello   harp   triangle

Try it out

1. Get into pairs. One of the pair needs to think of an instrument.

2. Click play

   Try right-clicking on the questions — the computer reads them out for you.

3. The other person has to ask questions about it — using the tree diagram.

4. After each question, click on "yes" or "no".

5. The database should find the answer.

Try the game again, but swap round so you both get a chance to use the computer.

Extra things you can do if you're feeling clever...

1. You can add pictures to the database to show what the instrument looks like.

   You can use pictures from clipart, from the Internet, from scanned photos, or photos from a digital camera. It must be a "bitmap" image though — that means the name of the picture will have to finish with .bmp

2. You can add sounds to the database to hear what the instrument sounds like.

   Creating your own sound files is a bit tricky, but there are a few stored in the program. Try out "boing.wav" — that's my favourite.

Unit 4C — Branching Databases

Databases

Databases are really important. You probably know something about them already.

A Database is a Program that Stores Information

Databases are programs that store information.

The information could include names, words, numbers and times.

The Database contains Records and Fields

All the information about one thing is stored in a separate record.

Before computers, each record was often stored on a card, like this one:

Monster Name:	**Dinkumsplodge**
Lives in:	**Cheesecakes**
Number of Heads:	**2**
Can fly:	**Yes**

Each record can have more than one piece of information.

Each separate piece of information is called a field.

There are Three Different Kinds of Field

A field could contain...

Name:	**Megan Chips**
Age:	**14**
Height:	**145 cm**
Do you like spam?:	**No**

...words,

...numbers,

...or a choice — here the choice is "yes" or "no".

Databases

① *What kind of program is great for storing information?*

....

② *Fill in the missing words in these sentences:*

A .... is a program that stores information. All the information

about one thing is stored in a separate .... Each record is

made up of separate pieces of information which are called ....

③ *What three kinds of information can be in a field?*

1. ....

2. ....

3. ....

④ *Look at my database of all my friends.*

Name: Sarah Wisecactus
Name: Eddie Topshuffle
Name: Enid Headfull
Name: Andy Pebbledash
Age: 8
Friends since: 1999
Favourite food: Sausages
Best feature: Good at pie eating
Worst feature: Tells rotten jokes

a. How many records are there in the database?

....

b. How many fields are there in each record?

....

Collecting Information

Information is much easier to use if you collect it in the right way.

Messy Notes can be Confusing

Obidiah Toenail,
13, blue eyes
likes chocolate,
fair hair
no gerbil

If everyone writes their details in different ways, it makes it much harder to use the information.

It's easier if everyone fills in a standard sheet that is the same for everyone.

Name:	Obidiah Toenail
Name:	Jenkin Catflop ...
Age:	14 ....
Hair colour:	Green ....
Eye colour:	Hazel ....
Favourite food:	Sprout custard ....
Do you own a gerbil?	Yes

A Questionnaire makes things Easier

Forms specially designed to collect information are called questionnaires.

When you enter information into a computer, each piece has to be entered in the same way.

It's much quicker to enter stuff if the questionnaire asks things in the same order as the fields of the database.

Name:	....
Age:	....
Hair colour:	....
Eye colour:	....
Favourite food:	....
Do you own a gerbil?	....

Collecting Information

① _Why are lots of messy notes bad?_

....

② _What is a questionnaire?_

....

③ _What order should the questions be in?_

☐ A: Alphabetical order.

☐ B: The same order as the fields of the database.

☐ C: An order of aubergine vindaloo from my local curry house.

④ _Which of these is a questionnaire?_

☐ A: ☐ B:

Name:	....
Favourite Fruit:	....
Favourite Goat:	....
Favourite Goat's Favourite Fruit:	....
Do you like yodelling?	....

Questionnaires

You can use a computer to make your questionnaires.

Some Database Programs let you make your Own Questionnaire

You could use a word processor to make a questionnaire, but some databases let you make them too.

I made this one with Junior ViewPoint:

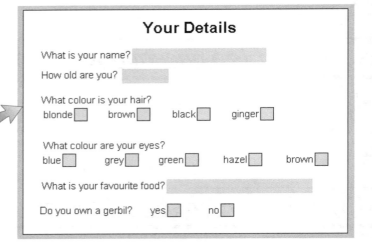

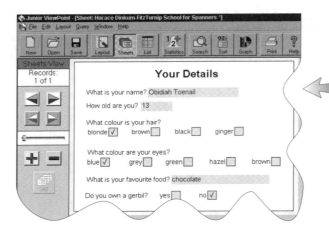

Here's what it looks like on the screen.

You can print out copies of your questionnaire, or you can just fill it in on the screen.

Use Tick Boxes when there are only a Few Choices

Computers are fast, but they're not as brainy as you. We know that "yes", "YES", "Y" and "yep" all mean the same thing, but a computer will treat them as different answers.

Drrrr!

✔ That's why it's a great idea to use tick boxes when there are only a few possible answers (e.g. like "yes" and "no").

✔ You can't spell a tick in different ways, so the computer won't get confused.

Questionnaires

① Which of these could you use to make a questionnaire?

☐ A: A word processor

☐ B: A database program

☐ C: A squashed cabbage

② When should you use tick boxes in a questionnaire?

....

③ What's wrong with the questions in this questionnaire?

What Are You Like?

What is your name? Henry McGee

How old are you? 10

Are you a boy or a girl? Yes

Do you like peas? Nope

What Are You Like?

What is your name? Amanda Bogglethribble

How old are you? 12

Are you a boy or a girl? Girl

Do you like peas? Not on your nelly, matey bubs

What Are You Like?

What is your name? Georgina Donut

How old are you? 11

Are you a boy or a girl? GIRL

Do you like peas? no

What Are You Like?

What is your name? Wilma Cargo

How old are you? 10

Are you a boy or a girl? I think so

Do you like peas? yeah

....

④ How could you improve the questionnaire above?

....

Charts and Graphs

Charts and graphs are a great way to show information.
They're much easier to read than lots of numbers.

There are Three Main Types

1. Pie charts

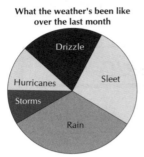

What the weather's been like over the last month

2. Bar charts

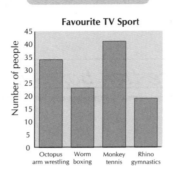

Favourite TV Sport

3. Line graphs

Height of Eddie the flying hippo after taking off from a cliff

Draw a Graph from a Database — It's Easy

① Press the **Graph** button.

② Choose which **fields** you want to use.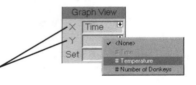

③ Choose the type of graph you want.

④ Hit the **Plot** button.

(Some databases will look a bit different from this, but they all work in a similar way.)

Make sure your Charts and Graphs are Easy to Read

When you draw a graph or chart, always give it a title.
If it has a title, then other people will know what it shows.

My Friends' Favourite Clothes

Always make sure the axes are labelled.

You can use different colours and shades to make it easier to read (and less boring).

Charts and Graphs

① Which is the best way to show this information?

☐ A: Things in My Last 11 Dreams

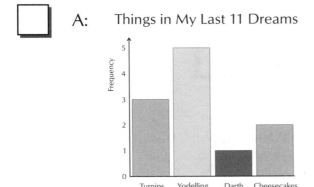

☐ B:

I dreamt of a yodelling hamster, then a huge pink turnip, then another yodelling hamster, then Darth Vader, then I had two dreams about cheesecakes, then two more about yodelling hamsters, two more turnip dreams, and finally another dream about yodelling hamsters.

② What are the 3 main types of charts and graphs?

1. ....

3. ....

2. ....

③ What kind of chart or graph are these?

Write **bar**, **line** or **pie** under these 3 graphs and charts.

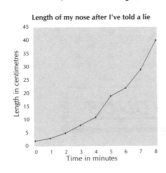

My friends' hobbies

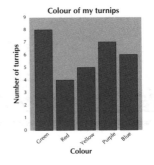

1. ....

2. ....

3. ....

④ Describe 3 ways you can make your graph easier to read.

1. ....

2. ....

3. ....

Pie Charts

You can use database programs to draw charts and graphs.
These make the information easier to read.

Pie Charts show how things Divide

How Jacob Spends His Day

Pie charts are great for showing fractions of things.

In this pie chart it's easy to tell that Jacob spends about a quarter of his time working.

It wouldn't be easy to tell that from a bar chart.

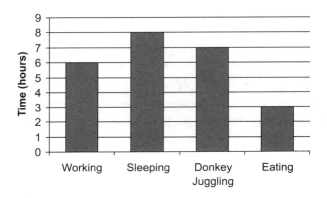

Pie Charts are great for Comparing Groups

It's easy to compare proportions of things using pie charts.

The Population of Dibblethwaite

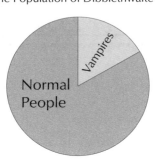

The Population of Hobblewidget

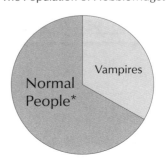

Here it's not hard to see which town has the greater fraction of vampires.

(But you can't actually tell which has more vampires, because you don't know which town is bigger.)

* and Herman Toasterwobble (Jr)

Pie Charts

① Reading Pie Charts

Answer the questions using these pie charts:

The Things People Hate Most

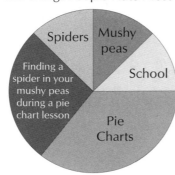

What Jane was Thinking About during her Pie Chart Lesson

1. What do people hate most?

....

2. For what fraction of Jane's lesson was she thinking of rabid walruses?

....

② Now compare these two pie charts:

Boys' Favourite Games at Flibflap School

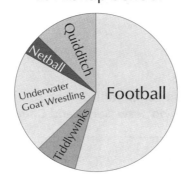

Girls' Favourite Games at Flibflap School

1. What game do the boys prefer?

....

2. Is Quidditch more popular with the boys or the girls?

....

Line Graphs

Line graphs and bar charts are other great ways to show information.

Bar Charts make Comparisons

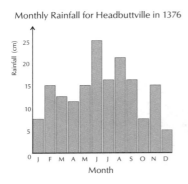

Bar charts are good for showing things that you want to compare.

On the bar chart to the left, it's easy to tell which months had the most and which had the least rainfall.

Line Graphs show things that Change Continuously

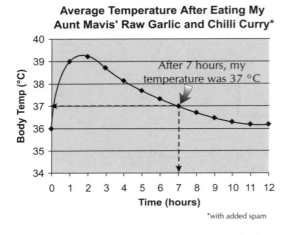

Line graphs are great for things which change smoothly, like temperature or someone's height.

You never see the temperature just jump from 10 °C to 20 °C — it goes through all the values in between.

If you used a bar chart, it would look like the temperature jumped from one bar to the next.

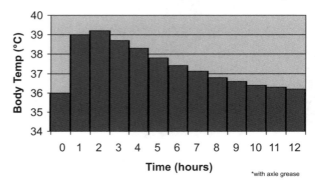

Line Graphs

① Reading Line Graphs

Answer the questions using these line graphs:

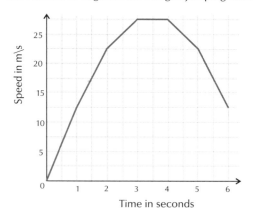

The Motion of Reginald the Bungee-jumping Snail

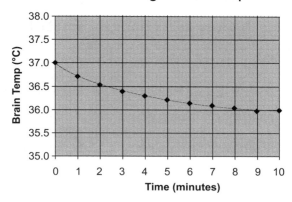

The Temperature of My Brain
After Drawing a Line Graph

1. What was Reginald's speed
    after 2 seconds?

2. How long was it before my brain
    fell to below 36.5 °C?

....

....

② Draw a Line Graph

The table shows my distance from home today when I tried to go out by pogostick.
Complete the graph to show my journey. (Or better still, get a computer to draw it.)

Time (minutes)	Distance (cm)
10	2
20	3
30	5
40	4
50	6
60	7

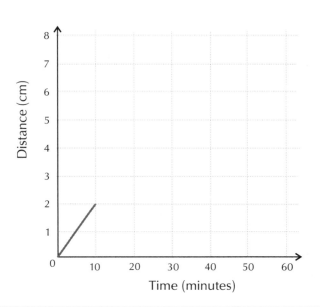

Charts and Graphs Project

In this project you will:

> *Investigate how the length of a shadow changes during the day.*

First get your results

You're going to see which kind of graph is best for showing the length of a shadow as it changes. First of all you need some results.

Time	Shadow length (m)
9:00 AM	4.8
10:00 AM	2.8
11:00 AM	1.6
12:00 PM	1.2
1:00 PM	1.5
2:00 PM	2.7
3:00 PM	4.5

> ✓ You could take your own measurements.
> But if it's cloudy or you can't make your own, use my results on the right.
>
> ✓ It shows the shadow made by a huge mouldy fossilised parsnip. But you can use a stick, if you like.

This is the distance you need to measure at different times during the day.

✹ You need to collect your results over a long time.
I collected mine between 9 am and 3 pm — that's 6 hours altogether.

✹ It's nice to take some readings in the morning and some in the afternoon.

✹ Take a new measurement every hour.

Now enter your results into a database

You need to set up your database first.

1. Your database needs 2 fields.

2. The first field will show the time. It's best to use the 24-hour clock for this. See the box on the next page if you're not sure about this.

3. The second field will show the length of the shadow.

Time	Length of shadow
9	4.8
10	2.8
11	1.6
12	1.2
13	1.5
14	2.7
15	4.5

Once you've set your database up, you can enter your results.
This is how my results look in Junior ViewPoint's 'List view'.

Charts and Graphs Project

Draw 3 different kinds of graph

This is where the fun begins. Use your database to draw 3 graphs
of your results — a pie chart, a bar chart and a line graph.

Length of Shadow

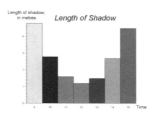

Length of shadow, in metres Length of Shadow

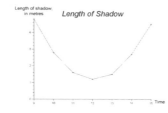

Length of shadow, in metres Length of Shadow

For the bar chart and
line graph, put 'time'
along the x-axis and
'length' up the y-axis.

Which one makes the most sense?

One of your graphs is better for showing the results of your 'shadow experiment' than
the other two. You need to decide which one is best. Use these questions to help you:

 Which type of chart is used for showing how something is divided up?
Is there a 'total amount' of shadow to divide up?

 Does the length of the shadow 'jump' from one value to the next?
Or does it change continuously?

 Which graph would tell me how long my parsnip's
shadow was at 9.30 am? Or at 2.15 pm?

Which type of graph is best for your shadow experiment? Give 2 reasons for this.

.... is best.

1. ....

2. ....

The 24-Hour Clock

Times before midday are easy in the 24-hour clock.

For example: 9 am = **09**:00, 10 am = **10**:00, 11 am = **11**:00, 12 midday = **12**:00.

Times after midday are a bit harder.

For example: 1 pm = **13**:00, 2 pm = **14**:00, 3 pm = **15**:00.

Just use the numbers in **bold** in your database.

For example, 9 am = **9**, and 2 pm = **14**.

The Floor Turtle

A floor turtle is a little robot which carries a pen.

You can use it to draw lines or shapes on a piece of paper.

The Floor Turtle is a little robot

You control the turtle with these commands:

forward 5 — The number tells the turtle how far to go.

back 4 — The number tells the turtle what angle to turn through. Here, it's 90°, then 180°.

left 90

right 180 — Pendown makes the turtle lower its pen to the paper. This means it will draw lines as it moves.

pendown

penup — Penup makes the turtle lift its pen from the paper. This lets you move it without drawing lines.

go — Go tells the turtle to do all the commands you've entered.

Watch the turtle follow this sequence...

I'm afraid my floor turtle is broken (I dropped a fridge on it).

So my pet turtle, Toby, will demonstrate how the floor turtle works.

SEQUENCE: **pendown   forward 3   right 90   forward 5   left 90   forward 6**

GO:

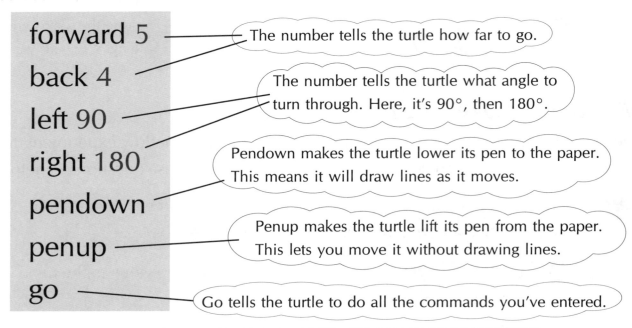

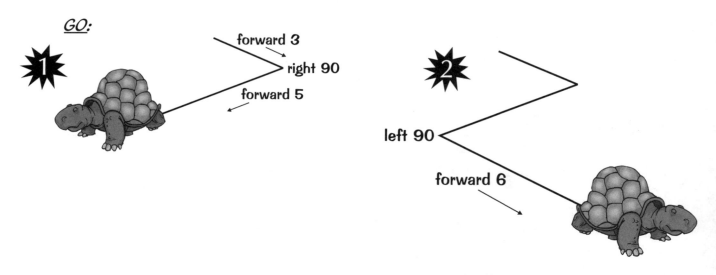

Very good, Toby.

The Floor Turtle

① What is a floor turtle?

Choose the correct words to complete these sentences.

A floor turtle is a small ....

that can be controlled using a simple list

of .... The turtle carries a ....

which can draw .... as it moves.

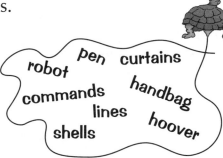

robot   pen   curtains   commands   handbag   lines   hoover   shells

② Put Lara back in her box.

Put the commands below in the correct order to guide Lara safely back into her box.

A left 45
B forward 10
C forward 3

The correct order is .... , ... , ...

③ How can I turn these turtles back to the start position?

Which command will turn the turtle back to the start position?
Draw lines to match each turtle to the correct command.

Start position

right 90   left 180   left 90

④ Scoop the poop.

Can you spot the turtle droppings on this page?
Draw a "poop scoop" around the droppings.

Like this.

Unit 4E — Modelling Effects on Screen

Using LOGO

From now on, we're going to use a <u>computer</u> turtle instead of a floor turtle.
You use a "LOGO" program to do this.

LOGO is a computer language

LOGO is a computer programming language. It lets you move a "turtle"
around the computer screen using the same commands as the floor turtle.

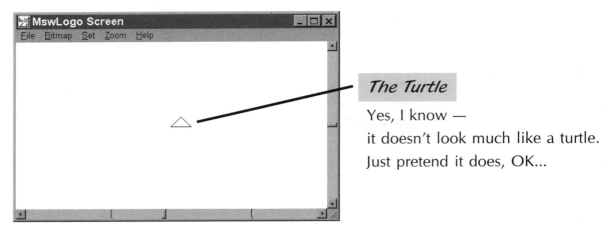

The Turtle

Yes, I know —
it doesn't look much like a turtle.
Just pretend it does, OK...

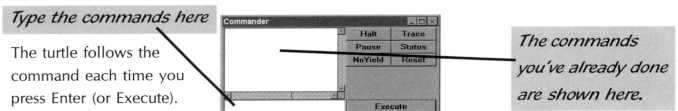

Type the commands here

The turtle follows the
command each time you
press Enter (or Execute).

*The commands
you've already done
are shown here.*

Use the same commands as the floor turtle

If you've used the floor turtle, you'll find LOGO really easy to get started with.
Here it is in action:

forward 100
left 90
forward 200...

...right 80
   back 100...

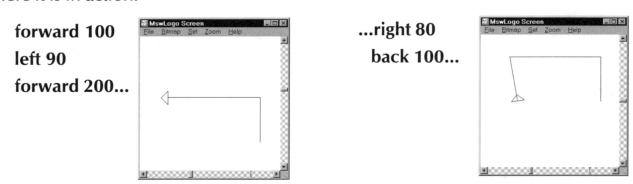

turtle tip

*In LOGO, you need to use **bigger numbers** to move the turtle*
— so instead of forward 3, you might use forward 50, say.

Using LOGO

① Can you label the bits of the LOGO program?

> turtle   commands already done   new command   scroll bars

Use the words in the bubble
to complete these labels.

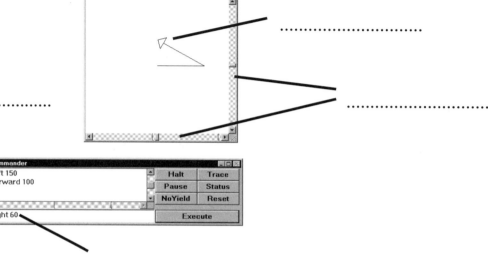

....

....

....

....

② What's different about the screen turtle?

Two of the sentences below say how the screen turtle is different from the floor turtle.
The other two sentences are rubbish. Put a tick ✓ next to the correct statements.

A You type **up** and **down** instead
of forward and backwards.

B You need **bigger numbers** to move
the turtle forward or backwards.

C Instead of typing **go**,
you just press **Enter**
after each command.

D The floor turtle can hula-hoop and
yodel at the **same time**. The screen
turtle can only do them separately.

③ Blimey, did you know...

*Some turtles can be as big as
two and a half metres long!*

*Turtles are older than Cilla Black
(and even most dinosaurs) — fossils have
been found dating back 200 million years!*

Using LOGO

Use Penup to move without making a line

If you want to move the turtle without drawing a line, use the command **penup**.

This makes the turtle lift its pen, so it won't draw as it moves.

When you want to draw again, type **pendown**. (It's just the same as the floor turtle.)

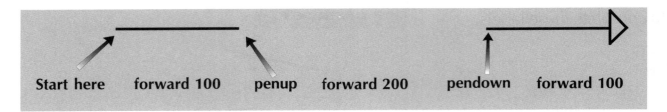

Start here　　**forward 100**　　**penup**　　**forward 200**　　**pendown**　　**forward 100**

"clear" and "home" are really useful

Here are two really useful commands that you'll need all the time.

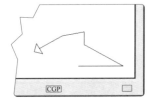 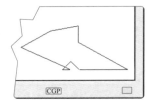 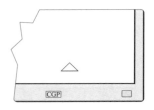

Here's a stupid doodle.

Home puts the turtle back where it started.

Clear wipes the screen. (sometimes it's called <u>clean</u>)

It's easy to draw basic shapes

Here are two shapes that you can do easily in LOGO.

<u>**SQUARE**</u>

forward 50
right 90
forward 50
right 90
forward 50
right 90
forward 50

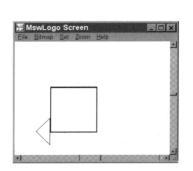

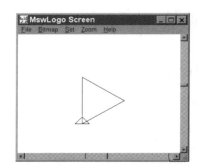

<u>**TRIANGLE**</u>

forward 100
right 120
forward 100
right 120
forward 100
right 120

turtle tip

*You have to be careful with **spaces** in LOGO.*
*Typing **"forward50"** won't work — it has to be **"forward 50"**.*
*Also, **penup** and **pendown** don't have spaces, so "pen up" won't work.*

Using LOGO

① Match each picture to the right commands.

Draw lines to match the
pictures to the command lists.

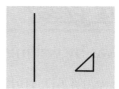 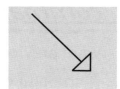 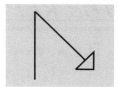

pendown	penup	penup
forward 80	pendown	forward 80
right 135	forward 80	right 135
penup	right 135	pendown
forward 80	forward 80	forward 80

② Spot the mistakes.

Some of the commands on the right have mistakes.
Draw a stinky fish around each mistake.

Like this

pen down

forward50

cleer

left90

back 400

home 5

penup

③ Help me to draw a staircase.

I want to make the turtle draw this staircase.
I've written the first four commands.
Can you finish the list of commands for me?

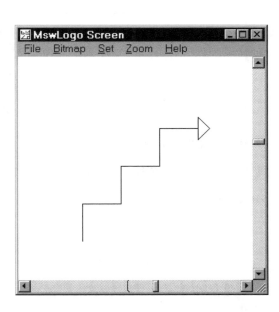

forward 50 ....

right 90 ....

forward 50 ....

left 90 ....

....

....

Repeating Things

It can get really annoying when you have to type in the same thing again and again.

The REPEAT command is great

The way we did a square previously was by writing out each separate command:

> forward 50, right 90, forward 50, right 90,
> forward 50, right 90, forward 50, right 90.

But this way is a pain because you're typing the same two commands again and again. A much better way to do it is with the repeat command.

repeat 4 [forward 50 right 90]
This says "repeat the bit in brackets 4 times".

Result — a lovely square, just like before but with far less typing, hurray!

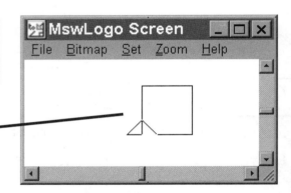

REPEAT lets you do shapes really easily

It's easy to make shapes with any number of sides:

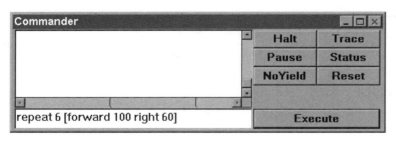

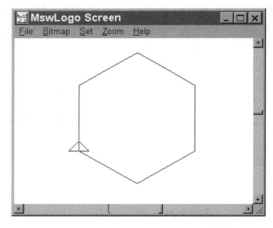

This gives a **6-sided** shape (hexagon).
That's because the bit in brackets draws one side and you repeat this 6 times.

Hey Mathmo...
To make a shape join up, you need to turn through 360° in total (a full circle).
Here, it turns 60° six times, because 6 × 60 = 360°.

Repeating Things

① What does the "repeat" command do?

Write "why aye, man!" under the correct answer.

> Like this
> *why aye, man!*

repeats what you type   **repeats a set of commands**   **eats holiday reps**

② What's wrong with these lines?

Below are two attempts to draw an octagon. Each has a mistake in it.

repeat 8   left 45   forward 30   ✘

repeat [left 45   forward 30]   ✘

Write down what it should be here:

.... ✓

③ How did I make these great shapes?

For each line below, say which shape (**A** – **D**) it would make.

repeat 5 [forward 100   right 72] would make shape ....
repeat 4 [forward 100   right 90] would make shape ....
repeat 8 [forward 100   left 45] would make shape ....
repeat 8 [forward 100   right 45] would make shape ....

> Go and try each one
> in your logo program
> — see if you're right.

 A
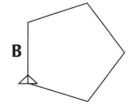 B
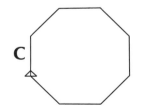 C
 D

④ How can I make this staircase using repeat?

Write a set of commands using repeat to draw this staircase.

....

....

Computer Activity — Making Patterns and Shapes

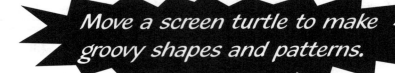

In this activity you will:

Move a screen turtle to make groovy shapes and patterns.

First of all, <u>open</u> your LOGO program, so you're ready to start.

Try out these commands

For each set of instructions below, <u>write down</u> what you think you will get.

Then <u>test them out</u> on your LOGO program and draw them in the boxes below.

Don't forget to type <u>clear</u> or press <u>reset</u> after each one.

1 **forward 80   right 90   forward 80   right 90   forward 80   right 90 forward 80   right 90**

I think it will be a .... **NOW TRY IT OUT**

2 **left 45   forward 100   right 90   forward 100   left 90   forward 100 right 90   forward 100   left 90   forward 100**

I think it will be a .... **NOW TRY IT OUT**

3 **forward 50   penup   forward 50   pendown   forward 50   penup   forward 50 pendown   forward 50   penup   forward 50   pendown   forward 50**

I think it will be a .... **NOW TRY IT OUT**

4 **right 90   forward 150   left 90   forward 150   left 90   forward 150 right 90   forward 150   right 90   forward 150**

I think it will be a .... **NOW TRY IT OUT**

Draw what you got for each one in these boxes:

1	**2**	**3**	**4**

Making Patterns and Shapes

Using REPEAT to do things quicker:

☀ A staircase

1. Type this in: **repeat 3 [forward 50   right 90   forward 50   left 90]**
    You should get a staircase with 3 steps.

2. Now, try <u>changing</u> the repeat number or the forward numbers.

    repeat 15 [forward 80   right 90   forward 50   left 90]

    I've changed this to 80.

    I've changed this to 15.

    GO ON , HAVE A GOOD FIDDLE

3. Explain how the staircase changes when you change the numbers.

    ....

    ....

    ....

☀ Polygon shapes

1. Try out each of the lines below:

    repeat 3 [forward 50   right 120]   — you should get a triangle.

    repeat 5 [forward 80   right 72]   — you should get a pentagon (5-sided shape)

2. Now see if you can make your own hexagon (6-sided shape).

    turtle tip

    The tricky bit is getting the correct angle to turn through.
    You need to divide 360° by the number of sides.

    Write how you do it here:

    ....

☀ OK then Brainypants, what is this going to be?

repeat 360 [forward 2   right 1]

NOW, SEE IF YOU WERE RIGHT

"Well it's obviously going to be a ...."

Procedures

This page is about <u>procedures</u>. Don't worry, it's not as hard as it sounds.

You can teach the computer new words

You can use **procedures** to "teach" the computer how to do something.

You write a set of commands — a **procedure** — and give it a **name**.

Then when you type in that name, the turtle follows those commands.

> I've taught the computer three new words — **ted**, **jack** and **dougal**.

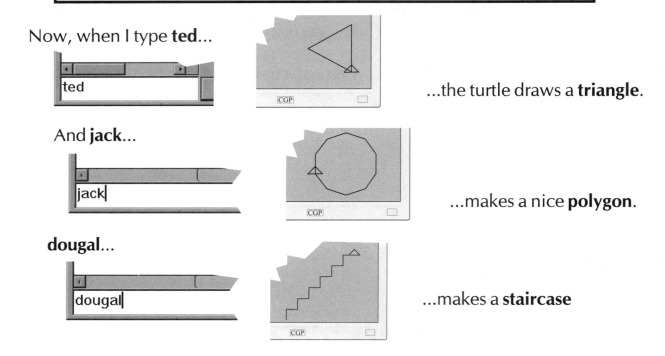

Now, when I type **ted**...

`ted`

...the turtle draws a **triangle**.

And **jack**...

`jack`

...makes a nice **polygon**.

dougal...

`dougal`

...makes a **staircase**

Use the new word whenever you like

When you've taught the computer a new word, you can use it whenever you like.

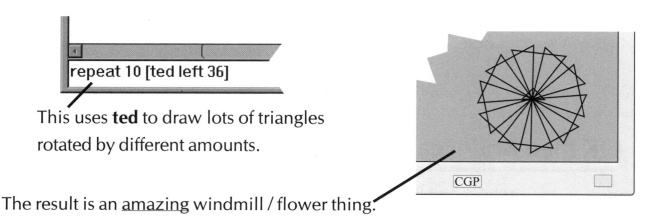

`repeat 10 [ted left 36]`

This uses **ted** to draw lots of triangles rotated by different amounts.

The result is an <u>amazing</u> windmill / flower thing.

And it only took one line of LOGO. If that doesn't excite you, I'm a poodle.

Putting in Procedures

① *What is a procedure?*

Fill in the blanks below.

> name   fishing   commands
> teaching   feeding   names

A procedure is a list of .... The turtle performs the commands when

you type the procedure .... Making a new procedure is like

.... the computer a new word.

② *Can you guess what this will do?*

I've made a procedure called **hobbit** which draws a **square** like this:

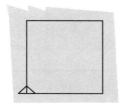

At the end of the procedure, the turtle is back exactly where it started.

Draw lines to match these LOGO commands to the right picture.

repeat 6 [hobbit left 60]

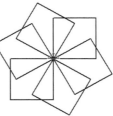

repeat 6 [hobbit left 20 forward 10]

③ *What do you think "pop" does?*

I've taught the computer a new word, "pop".
Now, when I type "**right 90 pop pop pop**" I get this:

Explain what the procedure "pop" does.
(If you're really clever, you could write the commands for it too.)

....

....

Making a procedure

This sounds really complicated, but it's not.

First Make a New Procedure

This is how to make the "ted" procedure from page 70.

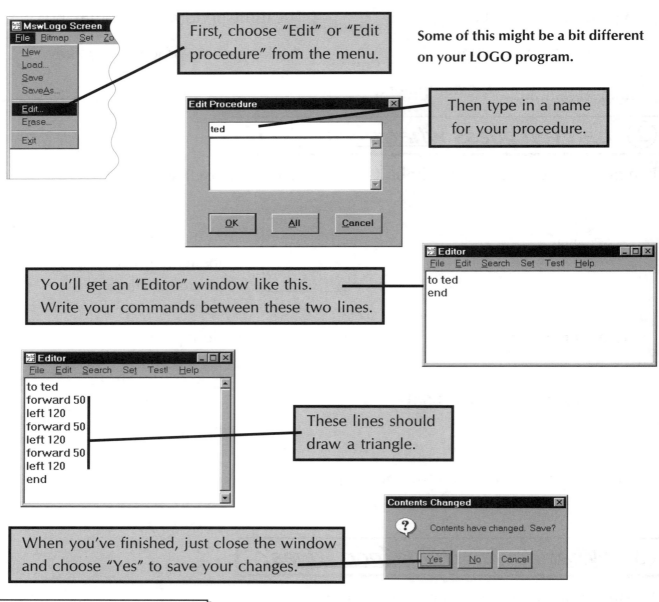

First, choose "Edit" or "Edit procedure" from the menu.

Some of this might be a bit different on your LOGO program.

Then type in a name for your procedure.

You'll get an "Editor" window like this.
Write your commands between these two lines.

These lines should draw a triangle.

When you've finished, just close the window and choose "Yes" to save your changes.

Now, test it out...

To see if it worked, type the procedure name in the command window and press <u>Enter</u>.

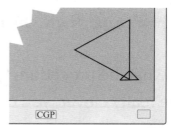

If it doesn't do what you expected, you can go back and <u>edit it</u>.

Using Procedures

① Which menu command is it?

Which command should I choose from
this menu to start a new procedure?

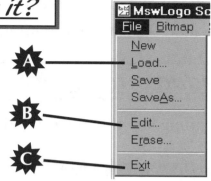

Answer ....

② Which of these is right?

One of these pictures shows how to correctly
put LOGO commands into a procedure.
The other two are wrong.

Draw a pair of underpants
beside each wrong picture.

 Like this.

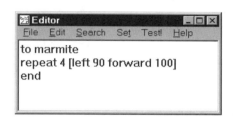

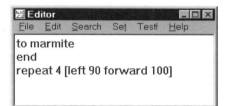

Make procedures to draw different letters

Procedures look scary, so get lots of practise using them:

Write a procedure called **LetterP** that draws a big letter **P**.
Check that it **works** by typing LetterP in the command window.
When you've done that, make a procedure for **each letter** of your initials.

This is tricky stuff — so if you can do this, I reckon you must be dead smart...

Making a Funky Flower

On this page, I'm going to make a funky flower — you'll never see a funkier flower, I can promise you that. Take my word for it, this flower will blow you away.

Write procedures for different parts of the flower

First of all, I'm going to write two procedures — **flowerhead** and **leaf**.

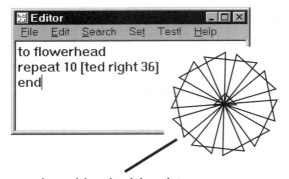

flowerhead looks like this.
(It uses the ted procedure that I made earlier to draw triangles.)

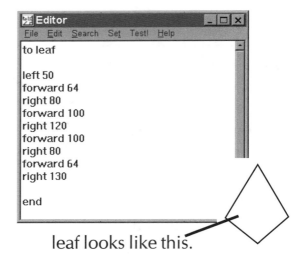

leaf looks like this.

Then put them together

Now all I need to do is write the commands to put these bits together.

To make the whole flower, I want to:
  1) draw part of the stem
  2) draw a **leaf** to the left
  3) draw a **leaf** to the right
  4) draw the rest of the stem
  5) draw the **flowerhead**

In LOGO, this could be...
  1) **forward 150**
  2) **left 80   leaf   right 80**
  3) **right 80   leaf   left 80**
  4) **forward 150**
  5) **flowerhead**

...and this is what you get. Wow...

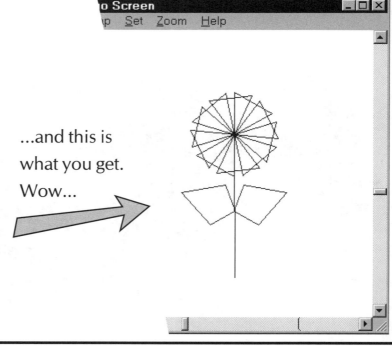

Making a Funky Flower

① *Draw lines to match the sequences to the flowers.*

forward 60   right 90   leaf   left 90   forward 140
right 90   leaf   left 90   forward 180   flowerhead

forward 100   left 45   leaf   right 45   forward 80
right 45   leaf   left 45   forward 200   flowerhead

flowerhead   right 60   forward 220   flowerhead
left 120   forward 220   flowerhead

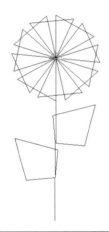      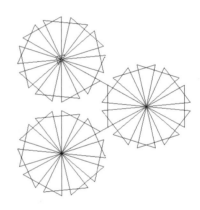

② *What does dobby do?*

If I change the flowerhead procedure to
use "dobby" instead of "ted", I get this:

Can you guess what "dobby" does?

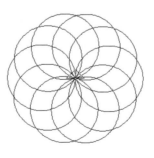

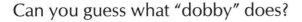

Doctor doctor, I've only got 59 seconds to live.

OK, I'll be with you in a minute.

Doctor doctor, I feel like a camera.

You'll snap out of it.

A man goes to a doctor with a banana up his nose and a carrot in his ear.

The doctor says he's not eating properly.

Unit 4E — Modelling Effects on Screen

Computer Activity

Draw a Snake

In this activity you will:

Create two procedures and put them together to make a snake.

Make a procedure called snakebit

1. Find the command to <u>edit a new procedure</u>.

   In MSW LOGO, you go to File, Edit and then type a name for the new procedure.

2. Start a new procedure called **snakebit**.

3. Type this sequence into the snakebit procedure.

   left 90   forward 25   right 120   forward 50   right 120
   forward 50   right 120   forward 25   right 90

4. Now type "snakebit" in the command window to test it.

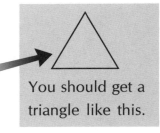

You should get a triangle like this.

Now make curlleft and curlright

You need to make two more procedures which will draw curly bits of the snake.

1. Make a procedure called **curlleft** with this sequence:
   repeat 20 [snakebit left 5 forward 5]

curlleft

2. Make a procedure called **curlright** with this sequence:
   repeat 20 [snakebit right 6 forward 5]

curlright

Now put them together to make a snake

That's all the hard work done. Now you're ready to make your own snake. I made mine like this:

   curlright   curlright   curlleft   curlleft
   curlright   curlleft   curlleft   curlright
   curlright   curlleft   curlleft

1. Draw your own snake using curlright and curlleft.

2. When you're happy with it, <u>print</u> it out.

3. Now <u>colour it in</u> and give it a <u>name</u>.

Make Funky Flowers

In this activity you will:

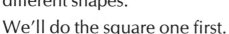
Combine procedures to make ACE flowers

Design a flower:

These groovy flowerheads are made by rotating different shapes.
We'll do the square one first.

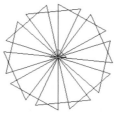 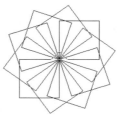 

triangle   **square**   **pentagon**

1. Teach the computer the word **square** which will draw a square.

    repeat 4   [forward 75   right 90]   **TEST IT TO SEE THAT IT WORKS**

2. Now teach the computer the word **flowerhead** which does this:

    repeat 10 [square   right 36]   **TEST THIS OUT — YOU SHOULD GET A FLOWERHEAD LIKE THE SQUARE ONE ABOVE.**

Make the leaf:

3. Teach the computer the word **leaf** to draw a nice leaf.
   The leaf procedure should have these commands in.

    **left 50   forward 64   right 80   forward 100   right 120
    forward 100   right 80   forward 64   right 130**

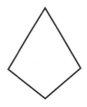

Use these to draw a flower

Make this flower using this sequence:

**forward 100
left 60   leaf   right 60
forward 50
right 110   leaf   left 110
forward 100
flowerhead**

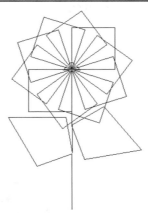

If you found that easy, try another one. You could put the leaves in a different place, or try the pentagon flower.

KS2 ICT Workout Series

- Covers the **KS2 ICT Scheme of Work** beautifully

- Ideal for use as   – **classbook**

                     – **computer activity book**

                     – **"at the computer" reference**

- Packed with **entertainment value**

- **Cheaper** than photocopied sheets — and **much nicer**!

ISBN 1 84146 458 9

9 781841 464589

I4R21

www.cgpbooks.co.uk